Soon, the little pea plants began to grow.

3

One day, Mum and Leo looked out
of the window.
There were lots of little birds in the garden.

Shoo!

Valerie Wilding
Illustrated by Garry Parsons

Mum and Leo planted some peas in the garden.

"The birds will eat our pea plants,"
said Leo.
"We must make the birds go away,"
said Mum.

Mum ran into the garden.
"Shoo, birds! Shoo!" she said.
The birds flew away.

The next day, the birds came back.
"I will make the birds go away,"
said Leo.

He went into the garden.
"Shoo, birds! Shoo!" said Leo.
The birds flew away.

flap! flap!

The next day, there were **big** birds.
"I will make the birds go away," said Leo.

He went into the garden.

"Shoo, birds! Shoo!" said Leo.

The birds flew away.

The next day, there were **bigger** birds.
"I will make the birds go away," said Leo.

He went into the garden.
"Shoo, birds! Shoo!" said Leo.
The birds flew away.

hoot! hoot!

The next day, there were **bigger birds.**

"Oh, no!" said Mum.
"These birds will **never** go away."

"Yes, they will," said Leo.

POP! POP! POP! went the pea pods.
The birds flew away.